This book belongs to

....

This edition published by Parragon Books Ltd in 2014

Parragon Books Ltd

Chartist House

15-17 Trim Street

Bath BA1 1HA, UK

www.parragon.com

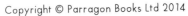

Written by Steve Smallman
Illustrated by Nicola Slater
Edited by Laura Baker
Designed by Ailsa Cullen
Production by Marina Blackburn

ISBN 978-1-4723-5094-7

Printed in China

PARROTS

GIBBONS

SPOT A LOT

AND COUNT
A LITTLE TOO!

ANIMAL ESCAPE

GIRAFFE

STEVE SMALLMAN   NICOLA SLATER

WARTHOGS

FLAMINGOS

PaRragon

Bath · New York · Cologne · Melbourne · Delhi
Hong Kong · Shenzhen · Singapore · Amsterdam

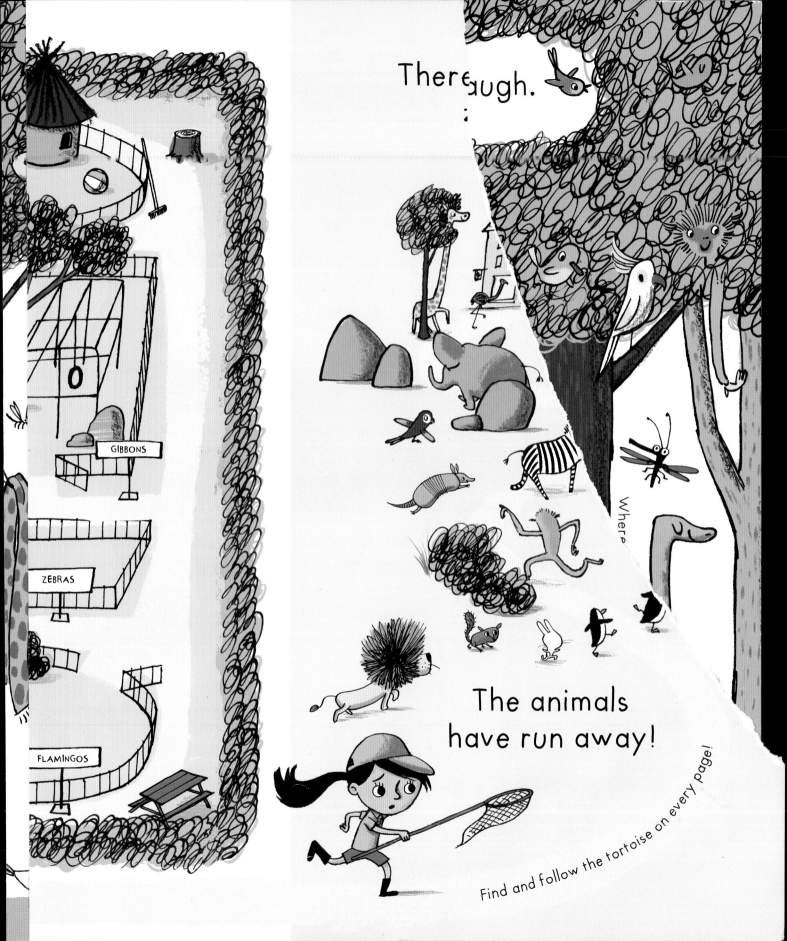

The animals
have run away!

Find and follow the tortoise on every page!

2 elephants in socks

playing
peek-a-boo
in the
rocks.

Where is the hippo hiding?

Peek-a-boo!

Spot 3 green lizards.

3 orange gazelles jumping high —

Find my 4 froggy friends.

they don't need trampolines to fly!

Spot the soaring dog – and his hat!

Spot 2 penguins doing backflips.

4 gibbons, long and slim,

Where is my second banana?

Who woke me up?

swinging by the jungle gym!

Spot the balancing lizard.

Who's in there?

Find the jumping mouse.

5 pretty pink flamingos

Spot the pink umbrella.

Find 4 slithering snakes.

6 zebras, white and black,

Spot the dog in a white hat.

crossing over the
road and back.

Spot 4 mice out and about.

Where's my other shoe?

7 batty little bats
wearing silly party hats.

Find a boot out of place.

Spot 10 pink birds
at the party.

Where is the little bumblebee?

8 penguins keeping cool

Where is my pink ball?

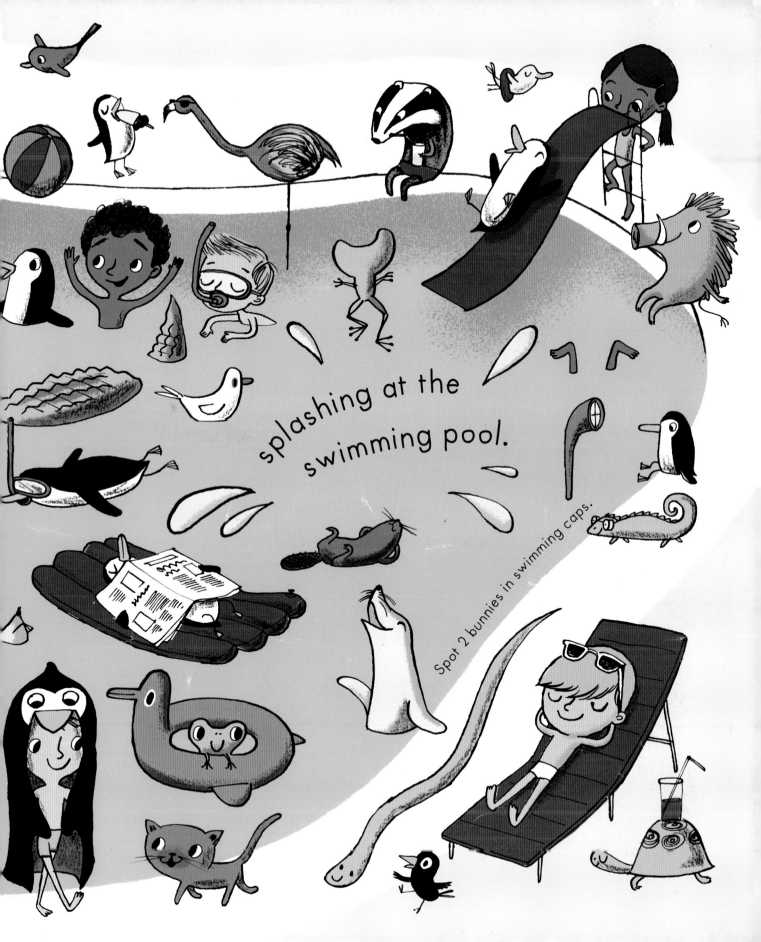

splashing at the swimming pool.

Spot 2 bunnies in swimming caps.

9 sneaky little parrots
hiding by the piles of carrots.

Find 2 frogs at the market stand.

Spot the little orange squirrel.

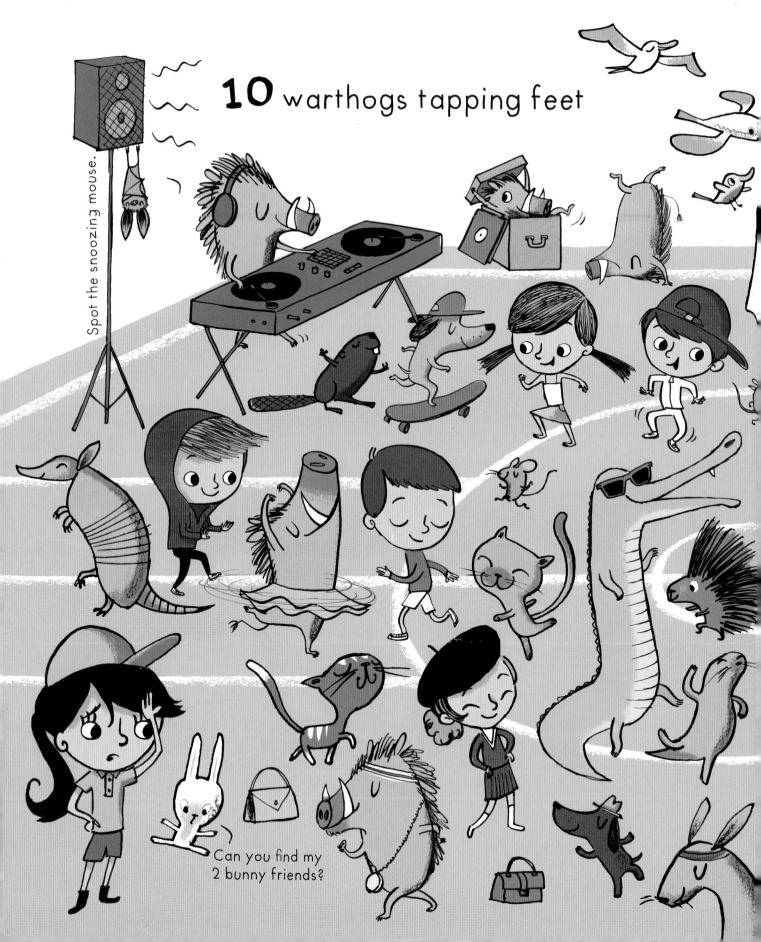

10 warthogs tapping feet

Spot the snoozing mouse.

Can you find my 2 bunny friends?

dancing to a hip-hop beat!

Find the fox
in sunglasses.

Where is my orange bag?

The keeper says,

"Let's have no fuss.
Now, everybody,
on the bus!"

Soon they're back
home in the zoo,

Spot the warthog who is still dancing!

GIRAFFE

WARTHOGS

GAZELLES

ELEPHANTS

BATS

PARROTS

GIBBONS

TORTOISE

PENGUINS

ZEBRAS

ZOO

FLAMINGOS

Spot the snorkelling penguin.

but uh oh, Tortoise, where are you?

THE END